Laura Shur

CONCERT TUNES
FOR THREE
for six hands at one piano

NOVELLO PUBLISHING LIMITED
8/9 Frith Street, London W1V 5TZ

Order No: NOV 100307

Concert Tunes for Three

These pieces are aimed at the pianist of Grade III to IV standard, as a vehicle for improving rhythm and balance of tone.

Playing the piano can be a lonely occupation, especially compared to the flute or violin which can be played in groups, but playing the piano with two other pianists has several advantages, namely:

a) it sharpens one's sense of rhythm;
b) it trains one's ear to listen to the balance of tone;
c) it increases one's responsibility to the other players, and therefore to one's own part;
d) it helps the shy pianist to play in front of others without feeling so vulnerable;
e) it improves concentration;
f) it adds the fun and joy of sharing a rehearsal and performance situation normally denied to the solo pianist.

Laura Shur wrote these pieces for her own piano pupils "to make them listen more carefully. Many parts of the body are involved in playing the piano, but ultimately it is the ear which has the final say in selecting the musical sound and the grading of tone."

Concert Tunes For Three is the fourth book in the *Tunes for Three* Series. Previous titles are:
Tunes for Three
More Tunes for Three
Christmas Tunes for Three

Thanks to this series, several Music Festivals are adding the piano trio to their list of entries, thus giving today's pianist the opportunity of taking part in ensemble playing.

Laura Shur studied piano with Phyllis Walker and Wight Henderson at the Royal Scottish Academy of Music. She followed graduation from the three year course in music education with a further year's study at Jordanhill Teacher Training College. The same year she gained the A.R.C.M. in piano performing and the L.R.A.M. in piano teaching. She has given many recitals, including a debut at the Royal Festival Hall, as well as BBC broadcasts and numerous duet recitals.

As a teacher, she has taught piano at the R.S.A.M., in schools and privately; and class singing and music up to A level.

Apart from the *Tunes for Three* Series she has composed piano duets, suites for string quartet, and wind ensemble as well as songs and choral music.

CONCERT TUNES FOR THREE

LAURA SHUR

1. MARCHING BY

PART A: Bass

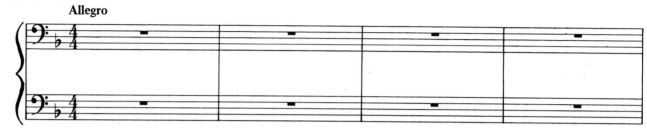

1. MARCHING BY

PART B: Middle

CONCERT TUNES FOR THREE

PART C: Top -
play one octave higher

1. MARCHING BY

LAURA SHUR

MARCHING BY (cont.)

MARCHING BY (cont.)

MARCHING BY (cont.)

2½ mins.

MARCHING BY (cont.)

MARCHING BY (cont.)

MARCHING BY (cont.)

2. JUST REMINISCING

PART A: Bass

2. JUST REMINISCING

PART B: Middle

9

2. JUST REMINISCING

PART C: Top -
play one octave higher

Andante teneramente

JUST REMINISCING (cont.)

JUST REMINISCING (cont.)

2½ mins.

3. RAGAMATAZZ

PART A: Bass

3. RAGAMATAZZ

PART B: Middle

3. RAGAMATAZZ

PART C: Top -
play one octave higher

'Ragamatazz' is played in the following order:

First 4 bars
Lines 2-3 & repeat
Lines 4-7 (triple section) & repeat
Lines 2-3 & repeat
Line 1 with 'last time' ending

RAGAMATAZZ (cont.)

RAGAMATAZZ (cont.)

RAGAMATAZZ (cont.)

4. TROPICAL BREEZE

PART A: Bass

4. TROPICAL BREEZE

PART B: Middle

4. TROPICAL BREEZE

PART C: Top

TROPICAL BREEZE (cont.)

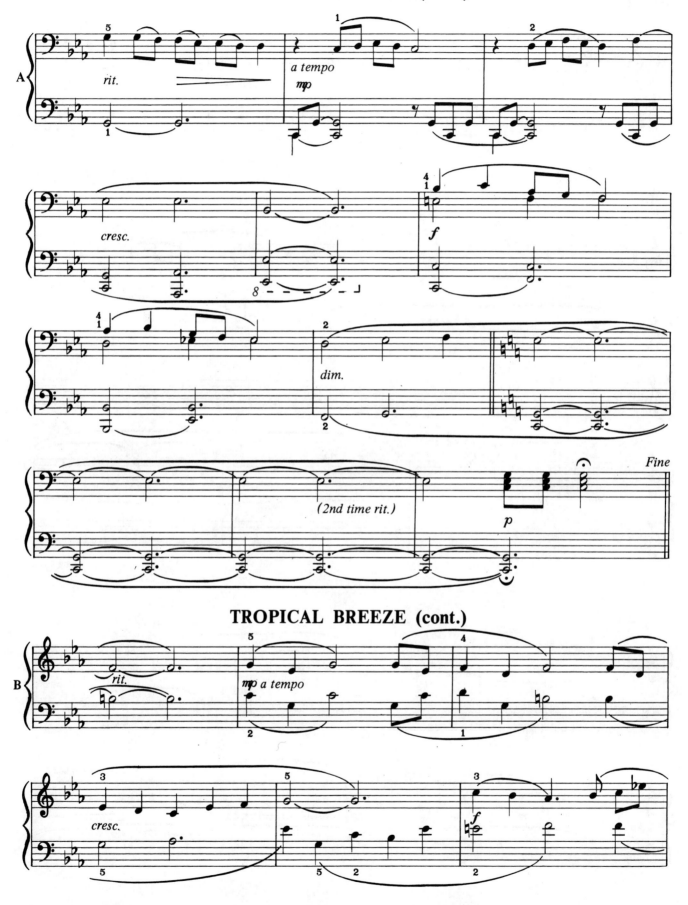

TROPICAL BREEZE (cont.)

TROPICAL BREEZE (cont.)

3 mins.

TROPICAL BREEZE (cont.)

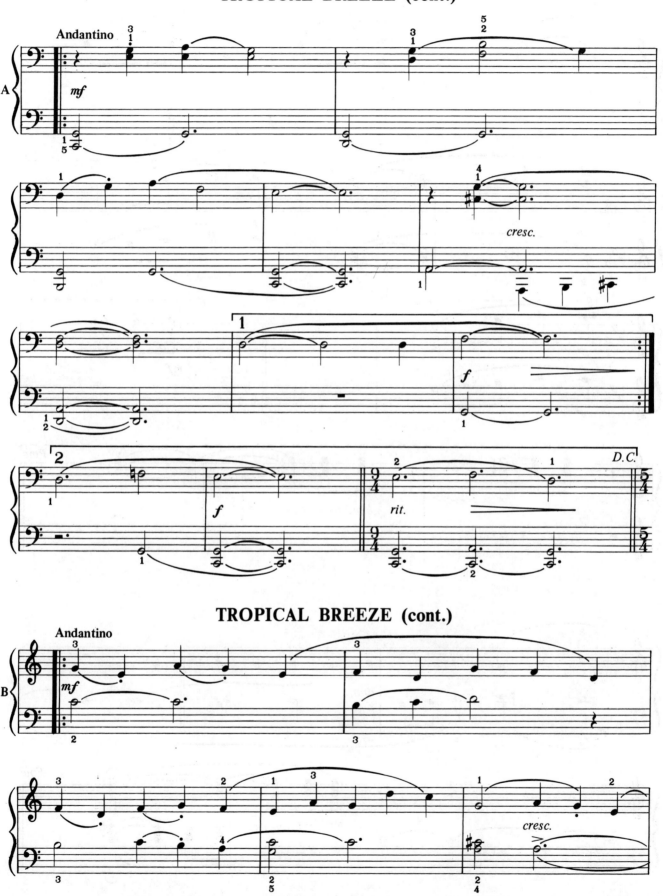

TROPICAL BREEZE (cont.)

TROPICAL BREEZE (cont.)

5. THE MERRY CUCKOO

PART A: Bass

5. THE MERRY CUCKOO

PART B: Middle

5. THE MERRY CUCKOO

PART C: Top -
play one octave higher

Comodo con spirito

THE MERRY CUCKOO (cont.)

THE MERRY CUCKOO (cont.)

THE MERRY CUCKOO (cont.)

1¾ mins.

Printed and bound in Great Britain by Headway Press Ltd

11/95 (22902)

Piano Music for Beginners

Piano Solo

Henry Duke
First Suite of Six Easy Pieces *(1)*
Second Suite of Six Easy Pieces *(1)*

Marjorie Helyer
Awayday *(Prelim 1)*
Down a Country Lane *(Prelim)*
Gay Pictures *(1)*
Over the Hills *(Prelim 1)*
Plum Stones *(2-3)*
Polka Dot *(2)*
Ship Ahoy *(2)*

Michael Hurd
Bagatelles *(3-4)*

Joan Last
Let's Play *(1)*

Kenneth Leighton
Pieces for Angela *(3)*

David Pratt
These you can Play *(2-3)*

Erik Satie
Children's Pieces *(2-3)*

Piano Duet

Marjorie Helyer
Contrasts *(3)*
Nimble Fingers *(1)*
Two's Company *(2)*

George Oldroyd
Miniature Suite of Duets *(2-3)*

Other Combinations

Phil Dennys
Three Way Stretch
for three players at one piano

Mary Sanders
The Junior Accompanist *(1-3)*
for piano with descant recorder
The Junior Accompanist *(1-3)*
for piano with treble recorder
The Junior Accompanist *(1-3)*
for piano with violin

Laura Shur
Christmas Tunes for Three
Tunes for Three
More Tunes for Three
for six hands at one piano

Numbers in brackets correspond approximately to the grading of the Associated Board.

402(88)